Garfield
Light Of My Life

JIM DAVIS

ℛℛ
RAVETTE BOOKS

First published by
Ravette Books Limited 1993

Printed and bound in Great Britain
for Ravette Books Limited,
8 Clifford Street,
London W1X 1RB
An Egmont Company
by Cox & Wyman Ltd, Reading

ISBN: 1 85304 353 2

© 1992 United Feature Syndicate, Inc.

© 1992 United Feature Syndicate, Inc.

JIM DAVIS 3-28

DARN GRAVITY

JIM DAVIS 4-1

© 1992 United Feature Syndicate, Inc.

© 1992 United Feature Syndicate, Inc.

© 1992 United Feature Syndicate, Inc.

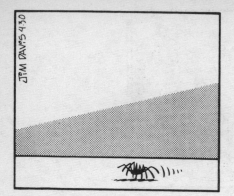

HE MUST HAVE HEARD
MY CONDIMENTS
CLINK TOGETHER

JIM DAVIS 5-9

© 1992 United Feature Syndicate, Inc.

© 1992 United Feature Syndicate, Inc.

© 1992 United Feature Syndicate, Inc.

© 1992 United Feature Syndicate, Inc.

© 1992 United Feature Syndicate, Inc.

© 1992 United Feature Syndicate, Inc.

ONE MORE TIME!!

© 1992 United Feature Syndicate, Inc.

© 1992 United Feature Syndicate, Inc

JiM DAViS 6-22

© 1992 United Feature Syndicate, Inc.

SNIFF

YOU'RE WEIRD!

CHECKING HIS BREATH FOR CANDY

JIM DAVIS 6-25

© 1992 United Feature Syndicate, Inc.

YOU'VE GAINED WEIGHT, BUT, HEY, WHO HASN'T?

© 1992 United Feature Syndicate, Inc.

THESE NEW TALKING SCALES WITH THE SYMPATHY CHIPS ARE GREAT!

JIM DAVIS 7-17

WE'RE OUT OF COOKIES!

AND I THINK THAT LAST ONE WAS A COASTER

JIM DAVIS 7-30

© 1992 United Feature Syndicate, Inc.

I HATE BIRDS

JIM DAViS 8-1

OTHER GARFIELD BOOKS IN THIS SERIES

GARFIELD COMIC ALBUMS

COLOUR TV SPECIALS

Here Comes Garfield	£2.95
Garfield On The Town	£2.95
Garfield In The Rough	£2.95
Garfield In Disguise	£2.95
Garfield In Paradise	£2.95
Garfield Goes To Hollywood	£2.95
A Garfield Christmas	£2.95
Garfield's Thanksgiving	£2.95
Garfield's Feline Fantasies	£2.95
Garfield Gets A Life	£2.95
Garfield's Night Before Christmas	£3.95
Garfield's Scary Tales	£3.95
Garfield Best Ever	£4.95
Garfield Diet Book	£4.95
Garfield Exercise Book	£4.95
Garfield Book Of Love	£2.99
Garfield Birthday Book	£3.99

All these books are available at your local bookshop or newsagent, or can be ordered direct from the publisher. Just tick the titles you require and fill in the form below. Prices and availability subject to change without notice.

Ravette Books, PO Box 11, Falmouth, Cornwall, TR10 9EN.

Please send a cheque or postal order for the value of the book, and add the following for postage and packing:
UK including BFPO – £1.00 per order.
OVERSEAS, including EIRE – £2.00 per order.
OR Please debit this amount from my Access/Visa Card (delete as appropriate).

Card Number ☐☐☐☐☐☐☐☐☐☐☐☐☐☐☐☐☐

AMOUNT £ ....   EXPIRY DATE ....

SIGNED ....

NAME ....

ADDRESS ....

....